I Remember

Pappy says:

"Never shoot at the bull's eye, shoot at the center of the bull's eye."

I Remember

Text and Pictures by
JOE CLARK, HBSS

Privately
printed for
The Tennessee
Squire
Association

Printed in the
United States of
America by
Kingsport Press, Inc.,
Kingsport,
Tennessee

Designed by
Gary Gore

Introduction

That Joe Clark is at it again, and all us
flatlanders can be grateful. It matters not a
tad what brand of adventures filled your
boyhood, or mine. They could hardly match
the ups 'n downs of young Joe as he grew
to manhood amid the vertical acres of his
beloved Tennessee. Therein, of course, lies
Joe's secret. There may just possibly be a detail
or two in this latest—and thoroughly enter-
taining—collection of Joe's recollections that
exceed verification. But the atmosphere, the
aroma, the lingo, the unself-conscious view of
the world—nobody could make these up.
The author had to live the life, and he had to
have an exceptional memory for recalling the
best of it. Joe Clark qualifies on both counts.

It happens they are building a miles-wide
Superhighway called Progress smack through
Joe Clark country. We are blessed to have
this delightfully authentic record of how it was.

TOM FLAHERTY
Associate Editor, Life Magazine

Most of us spent the days of our youth in some
community, state, or perhaps even country, other than
the one in which we now reside.
That community, the community of our youths, has been
softened by time and distance and mellowed in
memories and dreams until it has become, to us, God's
own little half-acre here on earth. And the only
difference between your home community and my home
community is that Tennessee really is God's little
half-acre.

—Joe Clark, HBSS

An explanation of words and terms for people who are not familiar with the English language.

STIR-OFF: Depends on the point of view; if you're old enough, it's for makin' soppins for the winter. If you're young enough, it's for makin' time with the girls. If you're a youngun it's for spying on the fellows and girls and reporting progress to the community at large.

WYOOTER: A Wyooter is similar to a geeflin except that it has one less toe on its hind foot. It is found only in desolate places by lone travelers on dark nights. A Wyooter can scare you to death just thinkin' about him. No Wyooter has ever been seen outside the state of Tennessee.

POSSUM: A critter that ain't worth much till you get him in a sack.

SASSAFRASS TEA: A brew for eliminating the weak.

MOUNTAIN DEW: A brew for eliminating the strong.

COURTIN': Trying to see how close you can walk to the edge of a cliff without falling off.

HOLLOW: A small valley

VALLEY: A big hollow.

MOUNTAIN: A big hill haired over with trees.

SORGHUM MOLASSES: Soppins for your winter biscuits.

POSSUM HUNTING: Like Wyooter hunting, only for kids.

POKE SALLET: A dish somewhat similar to plevin tongues and gorkel sprouts.

BEAN SHELLIN: An excuse for kids to get a little work and a lot of Sparkin' done.

CORN HUSKIN: Same as bean shellin' except it's played in the barn and seein how close you can come to the fire without gettin' burnt.

SPARKIN: Starting an uncontrollable fire by looking into a girl's eyes.

WALKING THE GIRL HOME: A slice of Heaven with cream and sugar on it.

HBSS

I remember...

. . . living
in an air-conditioned
house

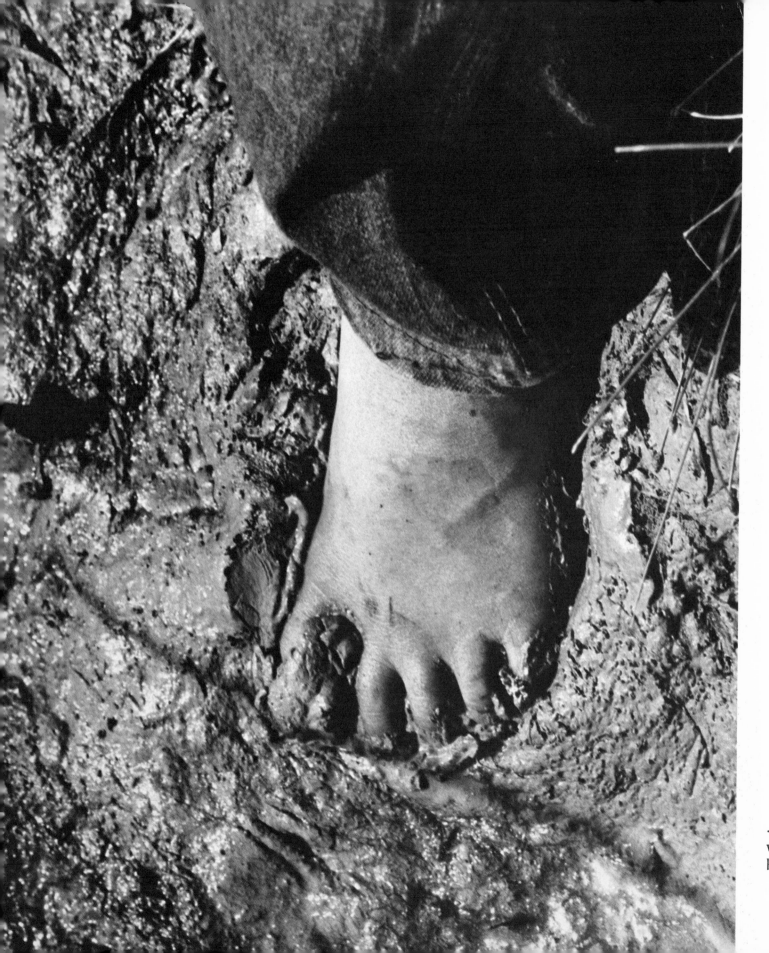

. . . squishing
warm spring mud
between my toes

. . . eating stolen watermelon

. . . daydreaming
in the
barn loft

. . . swimming
in the 'ole
swimming hole

. . . the
wonderment of my
baby sister

. . . and of
my sister's
wedding veil

. . . hunting with my old 12-gauge

. . . swinging on a grape vine

. . . catching fish
with my bare hands

. . . listening
to whippoorwills
at twilight

. . . stubbing
my toe
on a rock

. . . talking
with grandpa from
the barn loft

. . . driving up the cows at milking time

. . . riding down the creek road to the gristmill

. . . hoeing
corn in the hot
sun

. . . plowing
a mule in
a new-ground

. . . helping Ma
make a broom

. . . chopping stove wood

. . . playing town ball at the one-room schoolhouse

. . building myself a wagon

. . . drinking
cold spring water

. . . and dancin'
with a
pretty girl

. . . when
any man
with a grain
of spirit
could have a
business
of his own

I also remember...

Grandpappy Clark

Back in the early days my Grandpappy traveled all over this country in a covered wagon selling patent medicine. And he had this flock of trained pigeons that he used in his medicine show. So one day Grandpappy got his idea, and he trained his pigeons to fly upside down. Since in them days the science of animal and bird training had not yet been perfected, this was, in itself, quite a feat.

But Grandpappy didn't train those birds to fly upside down just to be horsing around. No sirreee! He was too practical a man for that. You see, back in those days there were very few bridges across the streams. And ferries were both scarce and expensive. Traveling across country in a covered wagon, Grandpappy found this to be quite a hardship. You never knew when the creek might be up or the ferryman not around.

So, after Grandpappy got his pigeons trained to fly upside down, he would simply drive up to a river and then reach back with his long driving stick and rap the side of the wagon smartly three times. This was the signal for those pigeons to get up and start flying around thus taking the load off the wagon. Then he would reach back and rap the wagon two more times. This was the signal for those pigeons to start flying upside down. All those pigeons flying upside down and fanning the wind upwards with their wings would cause the covered wagon to swell up like a giant balloon. And as soon as it was air borne Grandpappy would reach way back with his long driving stick and rap the very back end of the wagon. This would cause the pigeons to fly forward thus wafting the wagon right across the river as pretty as you please.

Grandpappy used this trick successfully for many, many years. And then one day a band of Blackfeet Indians was a chasing him. And Grandpappy and his covered wagon were a going full speed when they came to the Mississippi River.

So close behind him were those bloodthirsty Indians that Grandpappy saw that he wasn't going to have any time to stop the wagon and go through his usual pigeon ritual. But people were more resourceful back in them days. So Grandpappy just waited until he got exactly a hundred yards from the river then he reached back and rapped the side of the wagon smartly three times without even slowing down. This started the pigeons flying around taking the load off the wagon. And then when he got exactly one yard from the river he reached back and rapped the wagon two more times. This was the signal for the pigeons to start flying upside down, turning the wagon into a free balloon. Then one more rap way back on the back end of the wagon set her sailing over the old Mississippi as pretty as you please. And leaving them old bloodthirsty Indians stranded on the bank.

But just as Grandpappy got right over the deepest part one of them old Indians, who had always been known for being a poor sportsman, raised his bow and let fly an arrow right through the top of Grandpappy's covered wagon.

And that, dear friends, is how Grandpappy come to get drowned in the Mississippi.

And it is also generally believed to be the reason why Grandpappy's Pigeon Trick never caught on as well as it should have. And the reason why we've had to build so many expensive bridges over our streams.

Follow the Leader

Once when I was a boy my Pappy and me were driving some prize heifers out of the mountains where we had taken them to forage for the summer. The lead heifer, by some chance, took off on a narrow ledge that wound around the side of a cliff. Quite naturally all the other heifers followed her around the side of the cliff in single file.

We hadn't anticipated anything like this so neither of us had gone ahead to guard this side road. And so we had to stand by completely helpless and watch as the lead heifer came to the end of the ledge and kept walking.

Then, one by one, almost in slow motion, the entire herd of nineteen prize heifers walked off a hundred-and-sixty-foot cliff.

As the last heifer plunged through the treetops to the rocky slope below, Pappy turned to me and said, "Son, when we are handling stock, we always have to remember that cattle are just like people."

. . . following the leader

The Call of the Mountains

The call of the hills to the mountain child
  Is as strong as the call of love,
He may roam the world and explore the wild
  But return like a homing dove.

He may sail the oceans wide and blue
  And march over desert sands,
But for the mountain streams he'll always sue
  Though he be in distant lands.

He may roam the prairies bare and wide
  And ride the ranges free,
But he'll always sigh for the mountainside
  And his cabin in the lee.

He may visit the cities great and fair
  And see the sights so grand,
But he'll always long for the open air
  And the rolling mountain land.

He may see the things that all would see
  And roam the world in glory;
But he'll always yearn for Tennessee,
  The land of feud and story.

. . . the call
of the
mountains

Sittin' round the old gin'rl store

The wind was cold and the wind was rife
  And the stormy skies did weep;
The shavings on the floor in the gin'rl store
  Were a full three inches deep.

The fire in the stove was beginning to glow
  And the tales were tall and high
When he swore by his cloak that it wasn't a joke
  Nor would he stoop to a lie.

He bit off a chew and some smoke he blew
  And he spit on the red-hot stove,
Then he waited a mite for some peace and quiet
  And his trousers he gently hove.

Then all went quiet with sheer delight,
  We knew by the nod of his head
And the look in his eye as he breathed a sigh
  Some words were about to be said.

He cleared his throat, the sly old goat,
  And he sat back in his chair
Then he looked away to another day
  And he said with a gentle air:

  "Hit's gettin' cold outside."

. . . sittin' around the old general store

. . . riding
the hay wagon
at harvest
time

. . . the
gentle swish
of the
grain cradle
as my father
harvested wheat
by hand

. . . the chaff
from the thrasher box
on a hot day

. . . the thrashing dinner where hungry men downed mountains of food

. . . watching the Thresher-man make a few adjustments in his
storebought machine before getting under way for the afternoon

I'll never forget...

. . . sippin' new-made molasses at midnight

. . . when the folks would gather in from miles and miles around for the frolic

. . . square dancin' in the moonlight

. . . startin' a little sparkin' game

. . . the old timers who waited their turns to tell ghost stories

. . . kissin'
a girl at
stir-off

. . . the efficiency of the chaperones

. . chasing the girls in the canestalks

. . . and walking your girl home . . .

. . . by lantern light.

I'll always believe...

. . . in ghosts

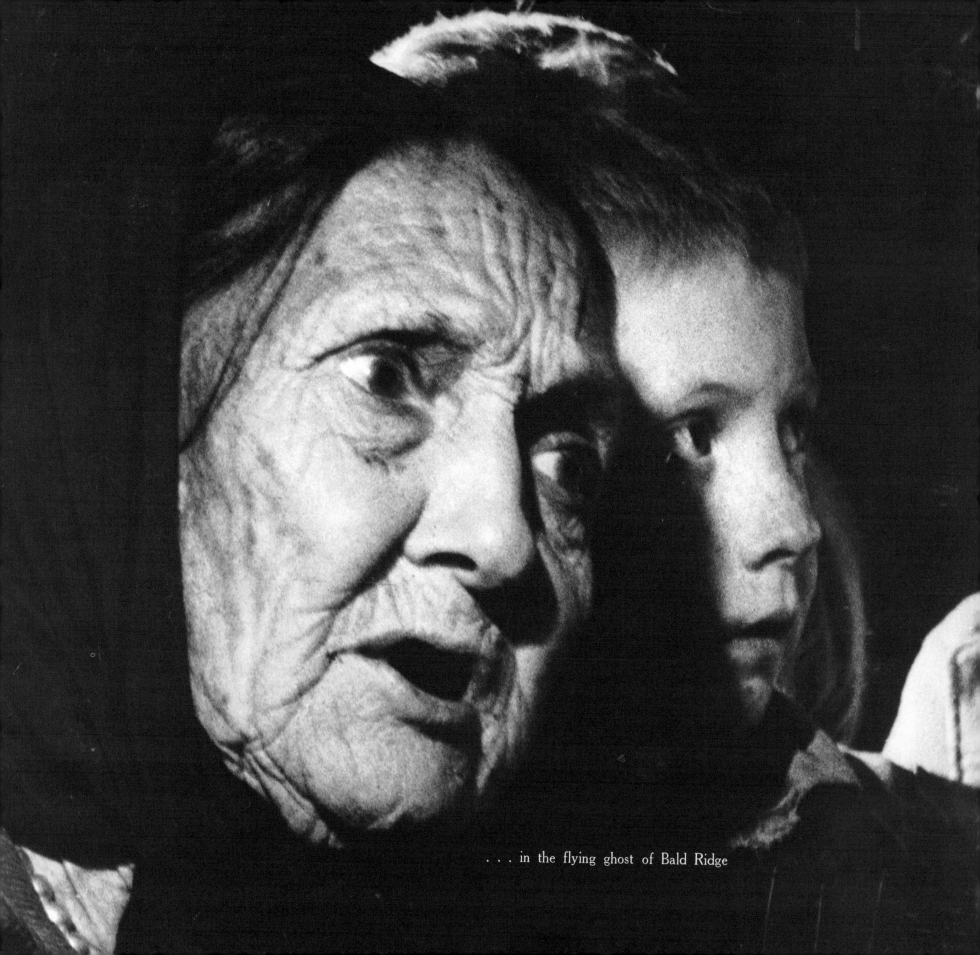

. . . in the flying ghost of Bald Ridge

It was one of them days. My prize heifer had just choked to death on a corncob, my dog got caught in a bear trap, and there was a rumor going around that Lucy had let Jimmie Humfleet walk her home from last night's stir-off, while I was out on a possum hunt.

I got to the stir-off early that night. I would show somebody who was walking Lucy home.

But my luck hadn't improved much. The pesky old mule that was pulling the cane mill kicked me and nearly broke my leg. On the first round of the square dance, I swung out too far and stepped in a full bucket of molasses.

When midnight came and we all gathered around the fire to watch the boiling molasses and listen to the old timers spin ghost stories, my head wasn't listening at all.

All I heard was a few odd bits and snatches from some kind of a yarn that Jesse McCrary was spinning: "It were exactly fifty years ago tonight . . . a night about like this . . . this is true facts . . . about eighteen inches tall . . . a strange sort of ghost . . . looked like an upside down soup bowl . . . had eyes all the way around . . ."

Lucy lived five miles up the valley, across Bald Ridge and all the way up to the head of Slocum Hollow. About a mile past where the Beasons used to live.

She said not a word on that whole trip home. My leg hurt where the mule kicked me, one of my shoes was still full of molasses, and I was mad at that no-good scoundrel for setting his bear trap where my dog could get caught in it. —So I wasn't much company either.

As we came to Lucy's house, I says to myself, says I, "We'll do a little settin' on the porch and get this thing all straightened out." But as we went up the front steps, Lucy took off and ran into the house and slammed the door. As I turned to head for home, her pappy's triflin', no-account houn dog snook out from under the porch and bit my backside.

As I mosied down Slocum Hollow, my mind had it all pretty well figured out: I would either jump in the river, or join the Foreign Legion. As I passed the house where the Beasons used to live, I wondered where they had moved to and whether Linda would feel sorry if she heard that I was killed by a cannonball in some lonely faraway land.

So nettled was my mind that I took a wrong fork going up Bald Ridge and got lost in the dark.

I was walking along the top of Bald Ridge looking for the right path when I heard this weird, wild and wonderful music, something akin to violins and silver bells, coming from a clearing up ahead. As I reached the clearing, the moon came out, and I could see these little purple people with red and yellow stripes that went both vertical and horizontal. They were a sort of metallic translucent color and seemed to glow faintly in the dark. And I couldn't really tell if they were standing on the ground or on the top of the tall blades of grass. They seemed to be singing and clapping their hands. Only I couldn't make out any words because their voices sounded more like violins playing than like people's voices. And as they clapped their hands, the sound was more like the tinkle of silver bells than like hand claps.

It was a sight more like you might see only in a dream. But I wasn't dreaming. I was wide awake and lost on top of Bald Ridge. And this fearsome ghost was standing, or sitting, at the edge of the clearing, looking for all the world like a huge soup bowl turned upside down, near as I could tell in the darkness. And it had eyes all the way around . . . only they looked a little like windows . . . except that they were round and seemed to glow with an eerie bluish light. It seemed to be hovering a couple of feet above the ground . . . not really touching it. And there was a soft purring sound, something like a cat . . . except that there was more of a whine to it. And occasionally it seemed to shiver a bit, as if it were cold . . . except that it wasn't a cold night.

It must have been my clumsy night; because, in my eagerness to get a closer look at these little purple people, I stepped on a dry twig. Instantly, the singing stopped and long ears not unlike metallic pencils popped up out of their little flat heads. For a moment I watched in petrified wonderment and then an owl hooted from a nearby tree. Who-o-sh, and they went bounding and bouncing like soap bubbles in the wind, straight for that monstrous ghost with the blue round eyes all the way around. They all scurried under it like a brood of chickens under a mother hen.

The instant they were all under it, this fearsome ghost scooped them up inside itself. And then . . . with an ear-splitting, spine-tingling shriek that sounded something like the wail of a wounded panther, it shot up into the air and away.

And if I had to die tomorrow, I would swear that it had a tail that looked like a long green flame of fire. So fast was its flight that it was out of sight in less time than it takes a possum to shinny up a 'simmon tree.

Look! There's blood on the moon tonight! That would have been a night like this one . . . exactly fifty years ago . . . Listen! Did that sound come from the direction of Bald Ridge?

. . . in wyooters

Wyooters are found
only in the hills of
Tennessee.
On dark and lonely nights.
They are easily the most
fearsome critters that
ever roamed the face
of the earth.

The Story of the Albino Wyooter

Before I was twenty-one, I had fished every stream from Keg Branch clear to Powell River. I had hunted possum on every ridge and in every hollow from Teetum's Gulley to Slocum's Knoll. And I'd seen everything from the head of Fearsome Valley all the way to the foot of Queezy Hollow; and, from the top of Bald Ridge to the far side of Gobbler's Knob.

I've been around some, in my time!

But of all the sights I've ever seen, I've never seen anything to compare with the night my houn dog, Old Trouble, tangled with the Albino Wyooter on Ghost Mountain.

It was one of them awful nights when the wind whips down the chimney, the sleet beats through the roof, and the milk clabbers in the springhouse.

I was on the far side of Ghost Mountain. Clear beyond Izzly Ridge in Gruesome Hollow. Most twenty mile from home. Hungry, tired, soaked to the skin. A cold steady rain was a-fallin, and dark was a-comin on. It wern't a fit night for man nor beast to be afoot.

Old Trouble sensed that everything in nature was wrong this night.

A black bear scurried acrost the path ahead. Old Trouble did no more than emit a low warning growl. A Panther wailed a shrill whining scream from a nearby tree. Old Trouble barely glanced up.

Owls and bobcats scurried about in a state of panic. Everything on foot or wing seemed gripped in terror. Old Trouble, sensing that we all faced a common danger, paid not the slightest heed to his natural enemies. He kept to the steep and narrow trail. Low to the ground. Tense as a steel trap. Ready to spring at the slightest warning. And I kept close behind, not really knowing whether the shiver in my bones was due to the cold driving rain or to the dread of the journey ahead.

Very few people had ever seen The Albino Wyooter. There was an Indian legend that it once swooped down on a band of Indians and carried off the Chief and seven Braves at one swoop. Then there was the time that Old Man Brown was crossing Ghost Mountain on horseback and The Albino Wyooter plucked his horse (bridle, saddle and all) from under him. Next day, his horse was found eating honeysuckle vines in a little hollow ten miles away. And years later it was claimed, but not by him, that Old Man Brown ran the twenty miles home in twenty minutes flat.

Many and fearful were the tales of The Albino Wyooter. It was white like a ghost, but it wasn't a ghost, because ghosts never molest animals. Certainly its feats of pulling up full grown trees or tossing huge boulders about couldn't be attributed to no ghost. Nosirreee! The Albino Wyooter was, without a doubt, the most fearsome whatever it was that ever roamed the Tennessee hills.

I inched up a little closer to Old Trouble as he angled up Izzly Ridge. He seemed to be shivering a bit. Maybe it was the cold. Old Trouble had no fear of man, beast nor varmint. But then The Albino Wyooter was neither man, beast nor varmint. Nor ghost for that matter. I couldn't blame Old Trouble if he shivered a bit.

We kept doggedly to the slippery and slimy trail, sometimes sliding or falling into the underbrush along the way. And perhaps startling a lynx or bobcat clear out of its wits in the bargain. But always we pulled ourselves together and got back onto the narrow and treacherous trail.

Ice, wind and rain had slowed our journey till it was just turning midnight as we started the awful climb up Ghost Mountain. It was now so dark I had to literally hang onto Old Trouble to keep with him. He had ceased to tremble. I could feel the hair bristle along his spine as he constantly sniffed the dank and foggy air. This would be a night to remember. If I lived through it.

Up and up we climbed. Over fallen timbers and broken boulders. Once, I thought I glimpsed the moon through the tall trees. It was something white. Pale white. Then the rustle of wings overhead. I listened intently. Then I shuddered. With a rain like this there could be no moon out tonight. Perhaps it was the cold, cold rain rustling in the leaves overhead.

We moved fearfully up the mountainside. Again, that white something over the treetops. Again Old Trouble bristled. There

. . . and in the albino wyooter

could be no mistake this time. It was The Albino Wyooter! ! !

My blood turned as cold as the icy rain that soaked my skin. Old Trouble kept on moving up the mountainside.

Facing certain death is one thing; but, The Albino Wyooter! ! ! There was no telling what might happen.

We were about to top the mountain when we felt the ground tremble beneath our feet. The Albino Wyooter had landed atop the mountain in a little clearing directly ahead of us. Its eerie, translucent form, tall as a tree, was silhouetted against the dark and threatening sky. Its giant claws were extended above its head. Its feet were planted far apart, and a poisonous mist emitted from its distended nostrils. It was drooling in anticipation of its coming feast. Its wild and weird eyes glowed with a sort of greedy bonechilling glow. As if it could taste us already.

There was a horrible sort of rumble, half growl and half chuckle, as one of its fearsome claws swooped down to scoop us up. Old Trouble jumped back so quick he sent me summersaulting over a huckleberry bush, as that fearsome claw scooped up a quarter yard of dirt and gravel where we had been standing but an instant before.

When The Albino Wyooter realized it had missed, it flung the dirt aside, and its whole giant frame quivered with rage and frustration. Its face turned seven different kinds of horrible purple. Its great square eyes seemed to turn into vats of boiling blood.

All my past life flashed before me in a single instant. I knew I would never catch fish in Keg Branch again. Or hunt possum on Pliny Ridge again. Or feast on cornpone and sow belly at Ma's table again. This time it would not miss. In its anger, it seemed to swell up to twice its normal size. The poisonous mist fairly hissed from its bursting nostrils as it crouched for the kill.

Suddenly with a snarl like giant thunder, that horrible claw swooped down like a streak of bent lightning. This time, Old Trouble didn't leap back. He sprang forward with such force that he lifted me off the ground as that fearsome claw grazed the seat of my pants and scooped up a full yard of dirt and two pine stumps where we had just been standing.

I knew my time had come. One more swipe and I'd be talking to Saint Peter face to face. I could feel them long sharp teeth biting through my tender hide already. I waited for the Wyooter to make its next grab. But, as that giant paw descended, Old Trouble made one last mighty lunge that carried us both through the great arch between that Old Wyooter's legs.

Suddenly, we were in the back of that varmint. Old Trouble had bested The Albino Wyooter.

Since Wyooters, once they've landed, can't turn around, we knew we were safe for the rest of the journey home. And when we got there, Ma had a feast of corn pone, sow belly and possum gravy waiting for us.

And it is said, that to this very day, The Albino Wyooter suffers from a case of acute frustration.

...in the simple things.

Sometimes I envy city kids all the worldly things they've got.
Yet, I can't help pitying the poor kid who has never

et a green persimmon,

chopped a rick of stovewood,

skinned a muskrat.

killed and plucked a chicken for dinner,

climbed an apple tree to get the last red apple at the very top,

stubbed his bare toe on a rock,

shook a big fat coon out of a tree,

drove the cows home at twilight,

picked wild strawberries,

took a turn of corn to the mill,

sat around a blacksmith shop,

turned a grindstone,

killed a mess of frogs with a homemade slingshot,

had a lizard run up the inside of his pantleg,

rode a wild yearling calf,

seen a real live ghost,

hoed a field of corn,

took a bath in a zinc washtub,

had a stonebruise on his heel,

squoze the warm spring mud through his toes,

went to town on the Fourth of July with a whole quarter
  to spend,

swung on a grapevine swing,

milked a muley cow,

smoked corn silks behind the barn,

walked a girl home from a spelling bee,

caught rabbits in a homemade trap,

chewed tobacco,

cut down a bee tree,

fastened his gallus with a rusty nail,

put a tadpole in the water cooler,

forked hay into a barn loft on a hot summer day,

stole a watermelon,

raised a calf,

sold a pig,

shot a squirrel,

picked a mess of poke sallet,

built himself a wagon,

rode a balky mule,

been lost in the woods at night,

stood alone on a mountain top in a pouring rain,

climbed a hill just to see what was on the other side,

had a dog named Old Trouble.

What will he have to remember?

Joe Clark, HBSS

We're only here a little while
And a long time we are gone
So come in and set a spell
Before you hurry along.